THE *Christmas* KEYBOARD SONGBOOK

MIKE CORNICK

UNIVERSAL EDITION UE 21 076

ISMN M-008-06425-8   ISBN 3-7024-0524-0   UPC 8-03452-00294-9

PREFACE

IN THE LATTER half of the 19th and the first few decades of the 20th centuries, the piano formed the centrepiece of domestic music-making in tens of thousands of homes in Europe, the USA and, indeed, in any other part of the world where Western influence and sufficient wealth made that a possibility. For a period of time, the keyboard skills of the domestic pianist were at a premium and the latent musicianship of many children must have been awakened by family 'sing-songs' around this wonderful and versatile instrument and by the piano lessons which many hoped would lead to its mastery.

Few could have foretold the fact that the technological advances which were eventually to displace the piano from this position of domestic prominence would also give rise to a completely new instrument – the keyboard synthesiser – and its baby brother, the electronic keyboard.

Electronic keyboards are now sold in vast numbers throughout the world and can be found in countless homes where no other musical instrument will ever be acquired. Many of these instruments become a temporary plaything, improperly understood and soon discarded. But increasing numbers of children and adults are beginning to realise the potential of these instruments and to recognise the worth of developing the skills needed to play them.

If, in domestic terms, the electronic keyboard is the 21st century equivalent of the piano, then Christmas must certainly be the time when it truly 'comes into its own'. And beyond the home, too, in schools, supermarkets and other public places, Christmas choirs now perform with the support of the electronic keyboard, exploiting its portability and the sophistication of its sounds and accompaniments.

If the advent of the electronic keyboard serves in any way to encourage participation in 'live' music-making, then its value will be beyond question.

MIKE CORNICK
March 2001

First published in Great Britain in 2001

Universal Edition (London) Ltd, London

UE 21 076

Cover design by Lynette Williamson

Cover photograph used with kind permission of Yamaha-Kemble Music (UK) Ltd.

CONTENTS

How to Get the Best from your Keyboard

THE MODERN ELECTRONIC keyboard is a sophisticated instrument which offers a wide range of accompaniments ('styles') which can be combined with an equally wide range of synthesised instrumental sounds ('voices'). Very often, the array of switches and buttons can be a little overwhelming and the following is intended to provide information and advice for those wishing to get started for the first time.

Keyboards vary from one manufacturer to another and from model to model. Have your keyboard handbook available so that you can check how the information offered here applies to your particular instrument.

Voice

This term refers to the instrumental sound which you want to hear from your keyboard. The information concerning these voices is usually printed on the instrument itself and grouped according to the type of instrument being synthesised, *e.g.* keyboards, strings, brass, *etc*. Each voice usually has a reference/selection number to provide quick access. In addition, there may also be some synthesiser voices (*e.g.* Square Lead) and some combination voices (*e.g.* piano and vibraphone). Some voices may be provided in harmony or there may be a 'harmony' button which allows you to add this option to existing voices. Keyboards usually default to a piano sound when first switched on. Select a voice.

Style

This facility may be given another name – perhaps 'rhythm' – but, however it is named, the options offered refer to the style of the accompaniment which you prefer to use, *e.g.* '8-Beat Ballad' or 'Bossa Nova'. Again, these options will be grouped and numbered. Select a style or rhythm.

Chord Function

The description of this function and the means of switching it on will vary greatly from one instrument to another. But in its simplest terms, we need to know how to select the lower section of the keyboard so that it will play an automatic accompaniment (in the style selected) according to the left-hand chord used. It may be just a function switch (where we are invited to switch between 'normal' or other automatic functions) or there may be an 'accompaniment on' button. We will also be offered the opportunity to make a synchronous start – *i.e.* to automatically start the accompaniment as we play our first left-hand chord, usually by pressing another button beforehand.

We may also have to decide whether we are going to play 'fingered' chords – *i.e.* to use triads or their inversions – in the left hand, or whether to use the 'brains' of the keyboard to figure out the detail of these chords by using the simplified 1, 2 or 3-key system of the instrument. This might be referred to as the 'single finger' function or may be given another name. According to these systems, a major chord can be played using one note (for C major, press C for example) and minor chords and added 7ths. (and even minor chords with added 7ths.) through the addition of other keys. You *must* consult your manual to find out how this works on your keyboard.

Some keyboards will accept both ways of playing these chords with no selection being necessary. Make your selections, and with any amount of luck, you should be in business!

Refinements

Some keyboards offer 'touch response', which means that they are velocity-sensitive: the faster you depress the key, the louder the sound produced. This function may be variable or you may prefer to switch it off.

You may also find buttons which play 'drum breaks' or 'fills' and you may have the facility to choose between alternative accompaniments within a style. You may also be able to choose which instruments are included in the accompaniment and to 'personalise' the accompaniment by reducing these. These options are helpful when using a less powerful 'lead' (right-hand voice).

Most useful of all, most keyboards offer a ready-made introduction and ending. If you simply press 'stop' at the end of a piece, the effect is of a very unmusical cut-off. Pressing 'ending' provides a more musical pre-programmed conclusion to the piece. The pre-programmed introduction gives a lead-in to the piece. Make sure that you start this in the correct key by playing the key (tonic) chord to start the piece. Guidance on this is provided for every piece in this book. The automatic introduction can be a useful facility, but it may not work very well if the melody begins on an 'up-beat'; for this reason (and because the style of the automatic introduction may be inappropriate) an alternative written introduction has been provided in each instance.

How to Make the Best Use of this Book

A box where you can note the style and voice numbers for your keyboard

Helpful advice on counting

Advice on keyboard settings: style, voice and tempo

| Style No. |
| Voice No. |

Away in a Manger
Music: William James Kirkpatrick
Words: Anon.

A helpful reminder about the key signature and any black keys which are needed

Suggested Style: Slow Waltz
Suggested Voice: Oboe
Tempo: 80 beats per minute

Count THREE beats in a bar. Notice that the written introduction and the melody begin on the 3rd beat of the bar.

We are in the key of F major. Look out for B♭, the black key to the left of B.

A written 'intro' to each piece

PLAY this introduction:

OR press INTRO. Start the keyboard introduction by playing a chord of F

Or use the advice to ensure you use the 'intro' button correctly

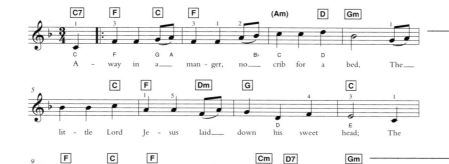

A clearly notated right-hand melody line with fingering to help you play accurately

All the lyrics for family singsongs or for those accompanying choirs in school or anywhere else this Christmas

Straightforward boxed chord symbols for 'fingered' or 'single-fingered' chords. Chord symbols in brackets offer alternatives or may be omitted

2. The cattle are lowing, the baby awakes,
   But little Lord Jesus, no crying he makes:
   I love Thee, Lord Jesus; look down from the sky,
   And stay by my side until morning is nigh.

3. Be near me, Lord Jesus; I ask Thee to stay
   Close by me for ever, and love me, I pray;
   Bless all the dear children in Thy tender care,
   And fit us for heaven to live with Thee there.

Alternative Terms

		BRITISH	AMERICAN		BRITISH	AMERICAN
Note	o	Semibreve	Whole note/rest	Note ♩	Crotchet	Quarter note/rest
Rest	▬			Rest 𝄽		
Note	♩	Minum	Half note/rest	Note ♪	Quaver	Eighth note/rest
Rest	▬			Rest 𝄾		

Bar = Measure

Away in a Manger

Music: William James Kirkpatrick
Words: Anon.

| Style No. |
| Voice No. |

Suggested Style: Slow Waltz
Suggested Voice: Oboe
Tempo: 80 beats per minute

Count THREE beats in a bar. Notice that the written introduction and the melody begin on the 3rd beat of the bar.

We are in the key of F major. Look out for B♭, the black key to the left of B.

PLAY this introduction:

OR press INTRO. Start the keyboard introduction by playing a chord of F

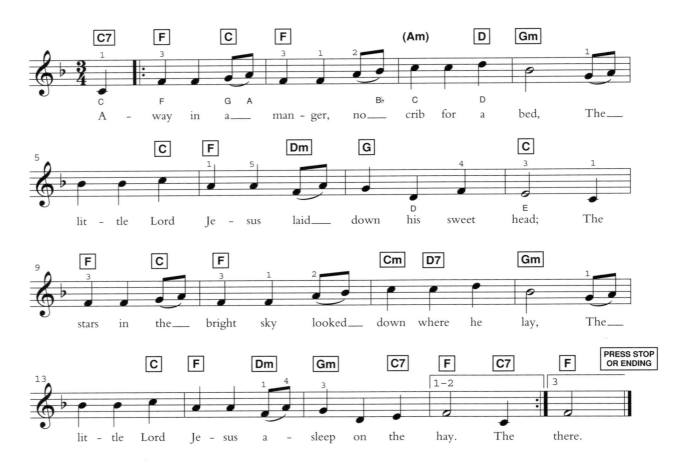

2. The cattle are lowing, the baby awakes,
But little Lord Jesus, no crying he makes:
I love Thee, Lord Jesus; look down from the sky,
And stay by my side until morning is nigh.

3. Be near me, Lord Jesus; I ask Thee to stay
Close by me for ever, and love me, I pray;
Bless all the dear children in Thy tender care,
And fit us for heaven to live with Thee there.

UE 21 076L

Style No.	
Voice No.	

Coventry Carol

Words and Music: Trad.

Suggested Style: Slow Waltz **Suggested Voice:** (French) Horn **Tempo:** c.92 beats per minute	Count THREE slow beats in a bar. Note that the written introduction begins on the 3rd beat of the bar.	We are in the key of E minor. Look out for F♯s, the black key to the right of F and D♯s the black key to the right of D. N.B. the melody ends on the major 3rd, G♯ (the black key to the right of G).

PLAY this introduction:

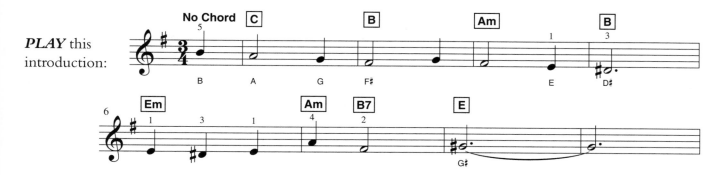

OR press INTRO. Start the keyboard introduction by playing a chord of E minor

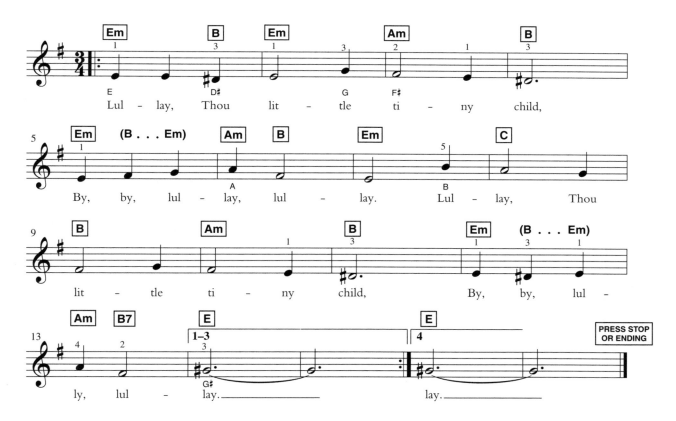

2. O sisters too, how may we do,
For to preserve this day?
This poor youngling for whom we sing,
By, by, lully, lullay.

3. Herod the King in his raging,
Charged he hath this day
His men of might, in his own sight,
All children young to slay.

4. Then woe is me, poor Child, for Thee
And ever mourn and say,
For Thy parting nor say nor sing,
By, by, lully, lullay.

UE 21 076L

| Style No. |
| Voice No. |

Deck the Hall

Music: Trad. Welsh
Words: Anon.

This carol exists in variant versions. A melodic alternative is shown in cue notation.

Suggested Style: Light Pop
Suggested Voice: Recorder & harmony
Tempo: c.80 beats per minute

This carol needs to move along at a bright tempo which calls for some quick chord changes.

We are in the key of F major. Look out for B♭s, the black key to the left of B.

PLAY this introduction:

OR press INTRO. Start the keyboard introduction by playing a chord of F

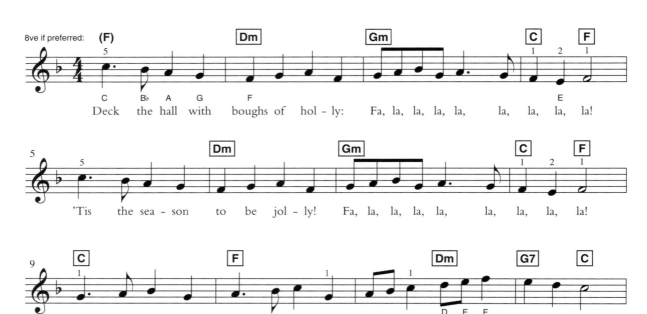

Deck the hall with boughs of hol-ly: Fa, la, la, la, la, la, la, la, la!

'Tis the sea-son to be jol-ly! Fa, la, la, la, la, la, la, la, la!

Fill the mead cup, drain the bar-rel, Fa, la, la, la, la, la, la, la, la!

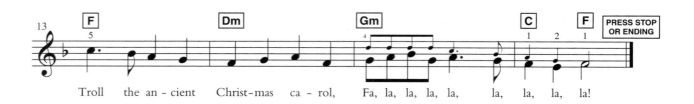

Troll the an-cient Christ-mas ca-rol, Fa, la, la, la, la, la, la, la, la!

2. See the flowing bowl before us!
   Strike the harp and join the chorus!
   Follow me in merry measure,
   While I sing of beauty's treasure.

3. Fast away the old year passes,
   Hail the new, ye lads and lasses!
   Laughing, quaffing, all together,
   Heedless of the wind and weather.

UE 21 076L

Ding! Dong! Merrily on High

Music: Thoinot Arbeau (1520-95)
Words: G. R. Woodward (1848-1934)

Suggested Style: 70's Disco
Suggested Voice: Synth Brass
Tempo: 130 beats per minute

We are counting FOUR beats in a bar. Note that the introduction begins on the "up beat." Play the first chord on the 1st beat of the next bar.

We are in the key of G major. Look out for F♯s, the black key to the right of F.

PLAY this introduction:

OR press INTRO. Start the keyboard introduction by playing a chord of G

2. E'en so here below, below,
    Let steeple bells be swungen,
    And 'Io, io, io!'
    By priest and people sungen.
    Gloria etc.

3. Pray you, dutifully prime,
    Your matin chime, ye ringers!
    May you beautifully rime
    Your evetime song, ye singers!
    Gloria etc.

The First Nowell

Words and Music: Trad. English

Style No.
Voice No.

Suggested Style: Slow Waltz
Suggested Voice: English Horn & harmony
Tempo: c.105 beats per minute

We are counting THREE beats in a bar. Note that the verse and the refrain both begin on the 3rd beat of the bar.

We are in the key of D major. Look out for F♯s, the black key to the right of F and C♯s, the black key to the right of C.

PLAY this introduction:

OR press INTRO. Start the keyboard introduction by playing a chord of D

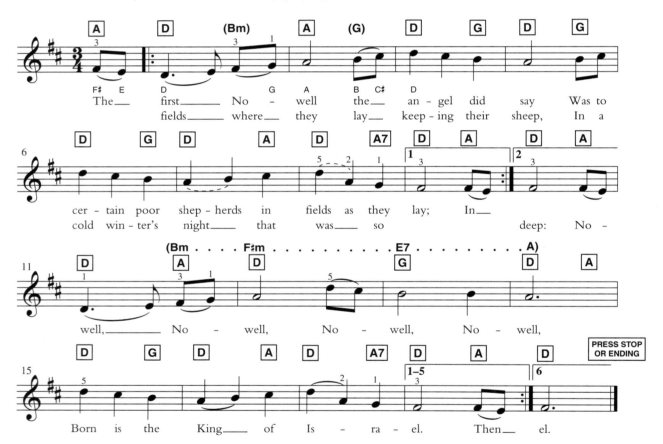

2. They lookéd up and saw a star,
Shining in the east, beyond them far;
And to the earth it gave great light,
And so it continued both day and night:
Refrain

3. And by the light of that same star,
Three wise men came from country far;
To seek for a king was their intent,
And to follow the star wherever it went:
Refrain

4. This star drew nigh to the north-west;
O'er Bethlehem it took its rest,
And there it did both stop and stay
Right over the place where Jesus lay:
Refrain

5. Then entered in those wise men three,
Fell reverently upon their knee,
And offered there in his presence
Both gold and myrrh and frankincense:
Refrain

6. Then let us all with one accord
Sing praises to our heavenly Lord,
That hath made heaven and earth of nought,
And with his blood mankind hath bought:
Refrain

10

Style No.
Voice No.

Go Tell it on the Mountain

Words and Music: Trad. American

Like many traditional songs, variant versions exist. Some alternative melody notes are shown in cue notation.

Suggested Style: Swing **Suggested Voice:** Voice (oohs) **Tempo:** c.140 beats per minute	Count FOUR beats in a bar and "swing" the quavers to fit the swing accompaniment.	We are in the key of G major. Look out for F♯s, the black key to the right of F.

PLAY this introduction:

OR press INTRO. Start the keyboard introduction by playing a chord of G

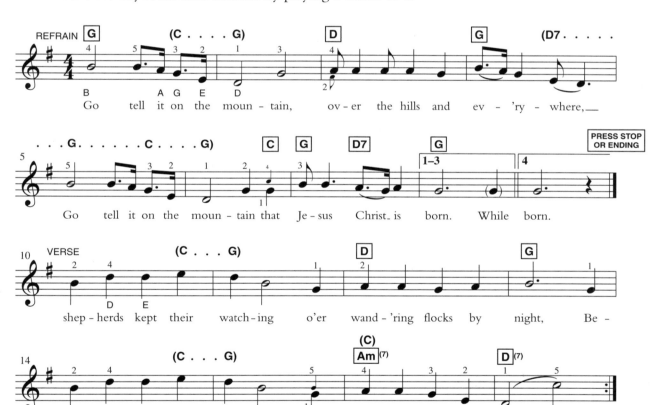

2. And lo, when they had seen it, they all bowed down and prayed,
   They travelled on together to where the babe was laid:
   Refrain
3. When I was a seeker, I sought both night and day;
   I asked my Lord to help me and he showed me the way:
   Refrain
4. He made me a watchman upon the city wall,
   And if I am a Christian, I am the least of all:
   Refrain

Style No.	
Voice No.	

Good King Wenceslas Looked Out

Music: Trad. English (13th C.)
Words: John Neale (1818-66)

Suggested Style: Pop Bossa **Suggested Voice:** Square Lead **Tempo:** c.140 beats per minute	We are counting FOUR beats in a bar. This carol needs to dance along and could be taken much faster.	We are in the key of G major. Look out for F♯s, the black key to the right of F.

PLAY this introduction:

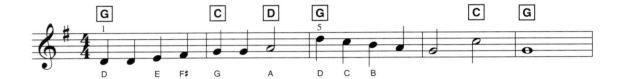

OR press INTRO. Start the keyboard introduction by playing a chord of G

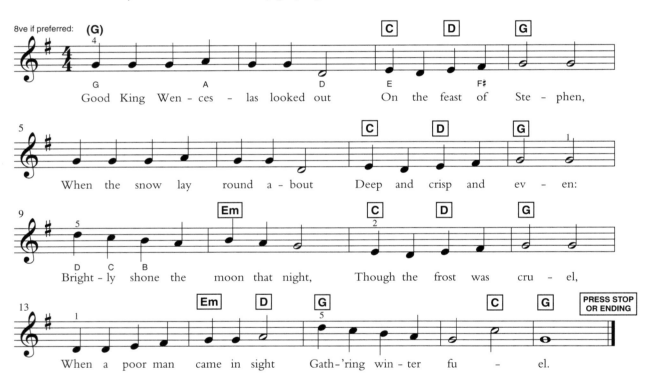

2. "Hither, page, and stand by me,
   If thou know'st it, telling,
   Yonder peasant, who is he?
   Where and what his dwelling?"
   "Sire he lives a good league hence,
   Underneath the mountain,
   Right against the forest fence,
   By Saint Agnes' fountain."

3. "Bring me flesh, and bring me wine,
   Bring me pine-logs hither,
   Thou and I will see him dine,
   When we bear them thither."
   Page and monarch, forth they went,
   Forth they went together;
   Through the rude wind's wild lament
   And the bitter weather.

4. "Sire, the night is darker now,
   And the wind blows stronger;
   Fails my heart, I know not how;
   I can go no longer."
   "Mark my footsteps, good my page;
   Tread thou in them boldly:
   Thou shalt find the winter's rage
   Freeze thy blood less coldly."

5. In his master's steps he trod,
   Where the snow lay dinted;
   Heat was in the very sod
   Which the Saint had printed.
   Therefore, Christian men, be sure,
   Wealth or rank possessing,
   Ye who now will bless the poor,
   Shall yourselves find blessing.

12

Style No.
Voice No.

Hark! The Herald Angels Sing

Music: Mendelssohn
Words: Wesley and others

Suggested Style: 16-beat Ballad	Count a steady FOUR beats in a bar.	We are in the key of G major.
Suggested Voice: Church Organ & harmony	N.B. the frequent chord changes.	Look out for F♯s, the black key to the right of F.
Tempo: c.90 beats per minute		

PLAY this introduction:

OR press INTRO. Start the keyboard introduction by playing a chord of G

Hark! the her-ald an-gels sing____ Glo-ry to the new-born King. Peace on earth and mer-cy mild,____ God and sin-ners re-con-ciled. Joy-ful all ye na-tions rise,____ Join the tri-umph of the skies,____ With th'an-gel-ic host pro-claim, Christ is____born in Beth-le-hem. *Hark! the her-ald an-gels sing Glo-ry____ to the new-born King.*

2. Christ, by highest heav'n adored,
    Christ, the everlasting Lord,
    Late in time behold Him come,
    Offspring of a Virgin's womb;
    Veiled in flesh the Godhead see,
    Hail, the Incarnate Deity,
    Pleased as man with man to dwell
    Jesus, our Emmanuel.
    Hark! the herald etc.

3. Hail the heav'n-born Prince of Peace!
    Hail the Son of Righteousness!
    Light and life to all He brings,
    Risen with healing in His wings;
    Mild He lays His glory by,
    Born that man no more may die
    Born to raise the sons of earth
    Born to give them second birth:
    Hark! the herald etc.

13

UE 21 076L

Style No.	
Voice No.	

The Holly and the Ivy

Words and Music: Trad. English

Suggested Style: Slow Waltz
Suggested Voice: French Horn
Tempo: c.90 beats per minute

Note that the verse begins on the 3rd beat of the bar. The refrain begins on the last quaver of the bar. Count "**1** and **2** and **3** and" playing the first G of the refrain on the final "and".

We are in the key of G major which includes the note F♯ However, no F♯s arise in the melody.

PLAY this introduction:

OR press INTRO. Start the keyboard introduction by playing a chord of G

The hol-ly and the i-vy, When they are both full grown, Of___

all the trees that are in the wood, The___ hol-ly bears the crown: *The*

ris - ing of the sun___ And the run - ning of the deer, The___

play - ing of the mer - ry or - gan, Sweet sing-ing in the choir.

2. The holly bears a blossom
   As white as any flower,
   And Mary bore sweet Jesus Christ
   To be our sweet Saviour:

3. The holly bears a berry
   As red as any blood,
   And Mary bore sweet Jesus Christ
   To do poor sinners good:

4. The holly bears a prickle
   As sharp as any thorn,
   And Mary bore sweet Jesus Christ
   On Christmas day in the morn:

5. The holly bears a bark
   As bitter as any gall,
   And Mary bore sweet Jesus Christ
   For to redeem us all:

6. *Reprise verse 1*

14

UE 21 076L

Style No.
Voice No.

I Saw Three Ships Come Sailing In

Words and Music: Trad. English

Suggested Style: Standard Waltz
Suggested Voice: Vibraphone
Tempo: Min. 180 beats per minute

Count THREE beats in a bar. You may prefer to use a 6/8 style which may sound more authentic. Simply read two 3/4 bars as one 6/8 bar and adjust the tempo accordingly.

We are in the key of G major. Look out for the F♯ which is the black key to the right of F.

PLAY this introduction:

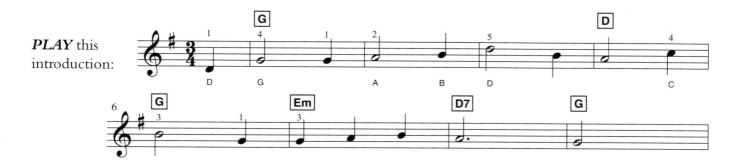

OR press INTRO. Start the keyboard introduction by playing a chord of G

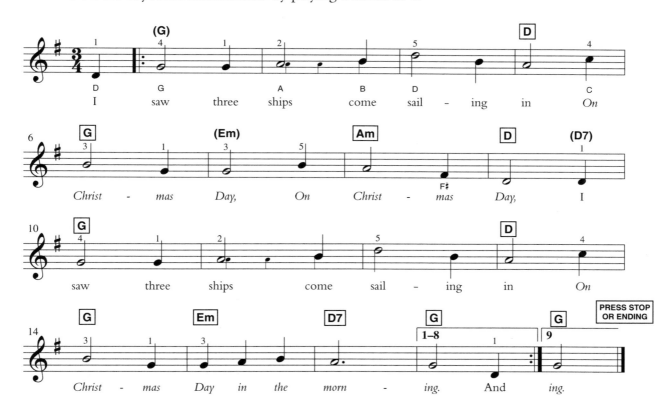

2. And what was in those ships all three?

3. Our Saviour Christ and his lady,

4. Pray, whither sailed those ships all three?

5. O they sailed into Bethlehem

6. And all the bells on earth shall ring

7. And all the angels in heav'n shall sing

8. And all the souls on earth shall sing

9. Then let us all rejoice amain!

UE 21 076L

In the Bleak Mid-Winter

Music: Gustav Holst (1874–1934)
Words: Christina Rossetti (1830–94)

Style No.
Voice No.

Suggested Style: Slow Rock
Suggested Voice: Ocarina
Tempo: c.84 beats per minute

Count a steady FOUR beats in a bar. If the carol is being sung, note the small differences in the verses. e.g. verse 1 begins on the first beat of the first bar but verse 2 begins with an up-beat.

We are in the key of F major. Look out for B♭s, the black key to the left of B.

PLAY this introduction:

OR press INTRO. Start the keyboard introduction by playing a chord of F

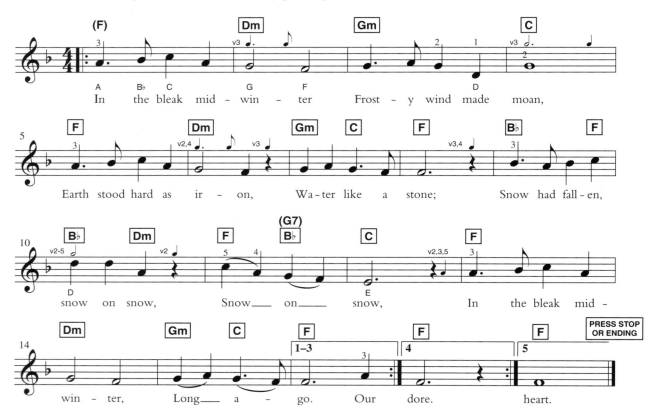

2. Our God, heav'n cannot hold him
   Nor earth sustain;
   Heav'n and earth shall flee away
   When he comes to reign:
   In the bleak mid-winter
   A stable-place sufficed
   The Lord God Almighty
   Jesus Christ.

3. Enough for him, whom cherubim
   Worship night and day,
   A breastful of milk,
   And a mangerful of hay;
   Enough for him, whom angels
   Fall down before,
   The ox and ass and camel
   Which adore.

4. Angels and archangels
   May have gathered there,
   Cherubim and seraphim
   Thronged the air:
   But only his mother
   In her maiden bliss
   Worshipped the Belovèd
   With a kiss.

5. What can I give him,   If I were a wise man
   Poor as I am?   I would do my part;
   If I were a shepherd   Yet what can I give him –
   I would bring a lamb;   Give my heart.

UE 21 076L

Jingle Bells
Short Version

Words and Music: James Pierpoint

Style No.		
Voice No.		

Suggested Style: 70s Disco
Suggested Voice: Electric Piano
Tempo: c.85 beats per minute
(treat crotchets as minims)

The time signature of 2/2 means that there are TWO minim beats in a bar. A 2/2 bar is equal in value to a 4/4 bar but has only **two** accents in each bar. Count "**1** and **2** and…" where **1** and **2** are minims.

This short version consists only of the well-known chorus and is set in the key of C major. No ♯s or ♭s are needed. Use the **transpose** function to change the pitch for singers if needed.

PLAY this
introduction:

OR press INTRO. Start the keyboard introduction by playing a chord of C

Style No.	
Voice No.	

Jingle Bells
Full Version

Words and Music: James Pierpoint

| **Suggested Style:** Pop Rock
Suggested Voice: Music Box
Tempo: c.150 beats per minute | Although we are using a 4/4 accompaniment-style, the feel of the piece is really 2/2, two minims in a bar. | We are in the key of F major. Look out for B♭s, the black key to the left of B. |

PLAY this introduction:

OR press INTRO. Start the keyboard introduction by playing a chord of F

Commonly, the up-beats in the verse are discarded:-

UE 21 076L

Mary Had a Baby

Words and Music: Trad. American

Many variants of this song exist. A few often-heard alternatives are included here.

Suggested Style: Swing
Suggested Voice: Drawbar Organ
Tempo: c.130 beats per minute

We are counting FOUR beats in a bar. "Swing" the quavers to fit the "swing" accompaniment.

Although set in the key of F, no B♭s arise in the melody line. (Pentatonic F G A C D)

PLAY this introduction:

OR press INTRO. Start the keyboard introduction by playing a chord of F

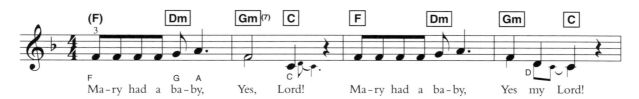

Ma-ry had a ba-by,   Yes,   Lord!   Ma-ry had a ba-by,   Yes my Lord!

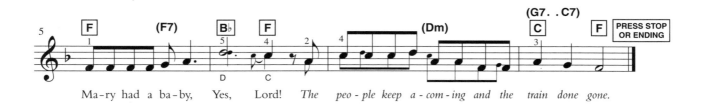

Ma-ry had a ba-by,   Yes,   Lord!   *The   peo-ple keep a-com-ing and the   train done gone.*

2. Where   did   she   lay him. *etc.*

3. Laid   him   in   a   man-ger, *etc.*

4. What   did   she name him? *etc.*

5. Ma-ry named him Je-sus, *etc.* or Named him King   Je-sus, *etc.*

6. Who   heard   the   sing-ing? *etc.*

7. Shep-herds heard the sing-ing, *etc.*

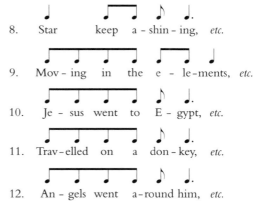

8. Star   keep   a-shin-ing, *etc.*

9. Mov-ing   in   the   e-le-ments, *etc.*

10. Je-sus went   to   E-gypt, *etc.*

11. Trav-elled on   a   don-key, *etc.*

12. An-gels went   a-round him, *etc.*

Tune and stanza 1 collected by N. G. J. Ballanta-Taylor in St Helena Island Spirituals 1925
(Penn Community Services Inc., South Carolina U. S. A.)

Style No.	
Voice No.	

O Christmas Tree

Music: Trad. German
Words: August Zarnack & Ernst Anschüt
English translation: Walter Ehret and George Evans

| **Suggested Style:** Trad. Waltz
 Suggested Voice: Oboe & harmony
 Tempo: c.90 beats per minute | Count a steady THREE beats in a bar. Note that the introduction and melody begin on the 3rd beat of the bar. | We are in the key of G major. Look out for F♯s, the black key to the right of F. |

PLAY this introduction:

OR press INTRO. Start the keyboard introduction by playing a chord of G

2. O Christmas tree, O Christmas tree,
Of all the trees most lovely;
Each year you bring renewed delight
A-gleaming in the Christmas night.
O Christmas tree, O Christmas tree,
Of all the trees most lovely.

3. O Christmas tree, O Christmas tree,
Your leaves will surely teach me,
That hope and love and faithfulness
Are precious things I can possess.
O Christmas tree, O Christmas tree,
Your leaves will surely teach me.

2. O Tannenbaum, o Tannenbaum
du kannst mir sehr gefallen.
Wie oft hat doch zur Weihnachtszeit
ein Baum von dir mich hoch erfreut.
O Tannenbaum, o Tannenbaum
du kannst mir sehr gefallen.

3. O Tannenbaum, o Tannenbaum
dein Kleid soll mich was lehren:
Die Hoffnung und Beständigkeit
gibt Trost und Kraft zu jeder Zeit
O Tannenbaum, o Tannenbaum
dein Kleid soll mich was lehren.

UE 21 076L

O Come, All Ye Faithful

Words and Music: from the M.S. of J.F. Wade (1711–86)

Style No.	
Voice No.	

Suggested Style: Pop Ballad
Suggested Voice: French Horn & harmony
Tempo: c.95 beats per minute

We are counting FOUR beats in a bar. Be prepared for four chord changes in some bars.

We are in the key of G major. Look out for F♯s, the black key to the right of F.

PLAY this introduction:

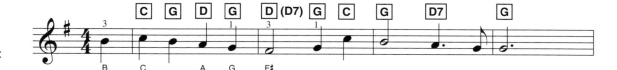

OR press INTRO. Start the keyboard introduction by playing a chord of G

2. God of God,
   Light of Light,
   Lo, he abhors not the Virgin's womb;
   Very God
   Begotten not created:
   O come let us etc.

3. Sing, choirs of angels,
   Sing in exultation
   Sing, all ye citizens of heaven above;
   Glory to God
   In the highest:
   O come let us etc.

4. Yea, Lord we greet thee,
   Born this happy morning,
   Jesu, to thee be glory given;
   Word of the Father,
   Now in flesh appearing:
   O come let us etc.

UE 21 076L

Style No.
Voice No.

O Little Town of Bethlehem

Music: Trad. (Forest Green)
Words: Phillip Brooks (1835-93)

Suggested Style: 8-beat Ballad	Count FOUR slow beats in a bar. The melody calls for frequent chord changes. A chord symbol in brackets may be disregarded.	We are in the key of F major. Look out for B♭s, the black key to the left of B.
Suggested Voice: Ensemble Strings		
Tempo: c.80 beats per minute		

PLAY this introduction:

OR press INTRO. Start the keyboard introduction by playing a chord of F

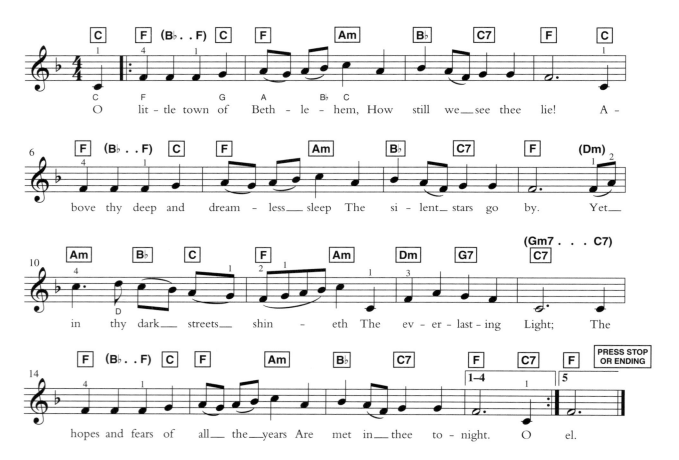

2. O morning stars, togther
    Proclaim the holy birth!
    And praises sing to God the King,
    And peace to men on earth;
    For Christ is born of Mary,
    And, gathered all above,
    While mortals sleep, the angels keep
    Their watch of wondering love.

3. How silently, how silently
    The wondrous gift is given!
    So God imparts to human hearts
    The blessings of his heaven.
    No ear may hear his coming,
    But, in this world of sin,
    Where meek souls will receive him, still
    The dear Christ enters in.

4. O holy child of Bethlehem
    Descend to us we pray;
    Cast out our sin, and enter in:
    Be born in us today!
    We hear the Christmas angels
    The great glad tidings tell;
    O come to us, abide with us,
    Our Lord Emmanuel.

UE 21 076L

Style No.	
Voice No.	

O Little Town of Bethlehem

Alternative Setting

Music: Lewis Redner (1831-1908)
Words: Phillip Brooks (1835-93)

Suggested Style: 8-beat light **Suggested Voice:** Halo pad **Tempo:** c.92 beats per minute	Count a steady FOUR beats in a bar. Note that the written introduction and the melody begin on the "up-beat", the 4th beat of the bar.	We are in the key of G major. Look out for F♯s, the black key to the right of F. We will also need some A♯s, the black key to the right of A.

PLAY this introduction:

OR press INTRO. Start the keyboard introduction by playing a chord of G

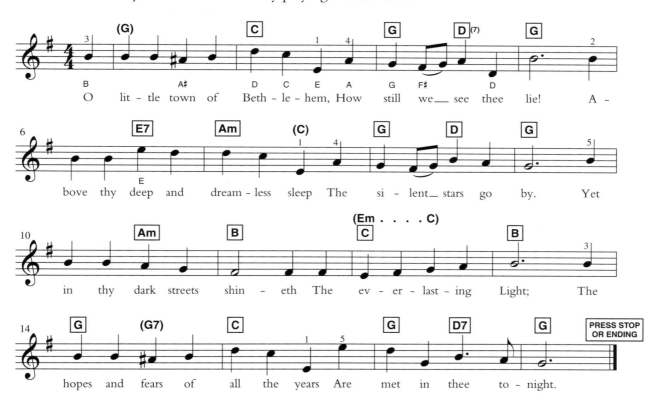

2. O morning stars, togther
    Proclaim the holy birth!
    And praises sing to God the King,
    And peace to men on earth;
    For Christ is born of Mary,
    And, gathered all above,
    While mortals sleep, the angels keep
    Their watch of wondering love.

3. How silently, how silently
    The wondrous gift is given!
    So God imparts to human hearts
    The blessings of his heaven.
    No ear may hear his coming,
    But, in this world of sin,
    Where meek souls will receive him, still
    The dear Christ enters in.

4. O holy child of Bethlehem
    Descend to us we pray;
    Cast out our sin, and enter in:
    Be born in us today!
    We hear the Christmas angels
    The great glad tidings tell;
    O come to us, abide with us,
    Our Lord Emmanuel.

UE 21 076L

Style No.
Voice No.

On Christmas Night

Words and Music: Trad. English (Sussex)

Suggested Style: 6/8 Rock★
Suggested Voice: Celesta
Tempo: c.65 (dotted crotchet) beats per minute

N.B. In 6/8 time, we are counting TWO (dotted crotchet) beats in a bar, each beat being worth three quavers. Notice that the melody starts on the last quaver of the bar: count **1** 2 3 **4** 5 6, so that the first melody note falls on 6.

We are in the key of G major. Look out for F♯s, the black key to the right of F.

PLAY this introduction:

OR press INTRO. Start the keyboard introduction by playing a chord of G

2. When sin departs before Thy grace,
   Then life and health come in its place;
   Angels and men with joy may sing
   All for to see the new-born King.

3. All out of darkness we have light,
   Which made the angels sing this night:
   Glory to God and peace to men,
   Now and for evermore, Amen.

*If your keyboard does not have a suitable 6/8 style for this piece then select a Waltz (3/4) style and double the tempo setting. Each 6/8 bar can then be treated as two 3/4 bars.

UE 21 076L

Style No.

Voice No.

Once in Royal David's City

Music: H.J. Gauntlett (1805–76)
Words: C.F. Alexander (1823–95)

Suggested Style: Light Rock Ballad
Suggested Voice: Choir
Tempo: c.85 beats per minute

Count FOUR beats in a bar. Use alternative accompaniment if available to create some variety from verse to verse.

We are in the key of F major. Look out for B♭s, the black key to the left of B.

PLAY this introduction:

OR press INTRO. Start the keyboard introduction by playing a chord of F

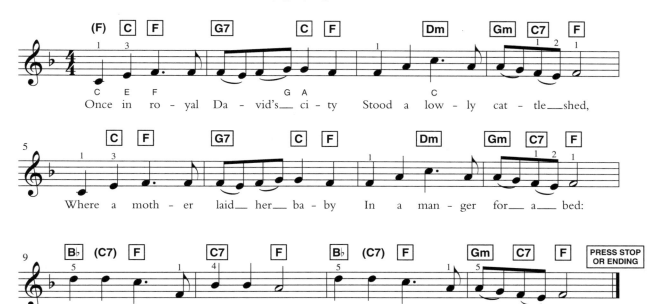

2. He came down to earth from heaven,
   Who is God and Lord of all,
   And his shelter was a stable,
   And his cradle was a stall;
   With the poor and mean and lowly
   Lived on earth our Saviour holy.

3. And through all his wond'rous childhood
   He would honour and obey,
   Love and watch the lowly maiden,
   In whose gentle arms he lay:
   Christian children all must be
   Mild, obedient, good as he.

4. For he is our childhood's pattern:
   Day by day like us he grew,
   He was little, weak and helpless,
   Tears and smiles like us he knew;
   And he feeleth for our sadness,
   And he shareth in our gladness.

5. And our eyes at last shall see him,
   Through his own redeeming love,
   For that child so dear and gentle
   Is our Lord in heaven above;
   And he leads his children on
   To the place where he is gone.

6. Not in that poor lowly stable,
   With the oxen standing by,
   We shall see him; but in heaven
   Set at God's right hand on high;
   When like stars his children crowned
   All in white shall wait around.

UE 21 076L

25

Rudolph the Red-Nosed Reindeer

Words and Music: Johnny Marks

Style No.	
Voice No.	

Suggested Style: Polka
Suggested Voice: Celesta
Tempo: c.88 (minim) beats per minute

Count TWO minim beats in a bar. This song should move along at a bright tempo and also works well in swing style (♫ = ♩♪)

We are in the key of C major. There are no black keys in the melody line.

PLAY this introduction:

OR press INTRO. Start the keyboard introduction by playing a chord of C

UE 21 076L

Shepherds' Rocking Carol

Music: Trad. Czech
Words: translated by Elizabeth Poston

Suggested Style: 8-beat Ballad
Suggested Voice: String Ensemble
Tempo: c.75 beats per minute

Count FOUR slow beats in a bar, remembering that, in an 8-beat ballad, we will hear 8 quavers in every bar. Count **1** and **2** and **3** and **4** and.

We are in the key of F major. Look out for B♭s, the black key to the left of B, but take care: not all Bs are flat.

PLAY this introduction:

OR press INTRO. Start the keyboard introduction by playing a chord of F

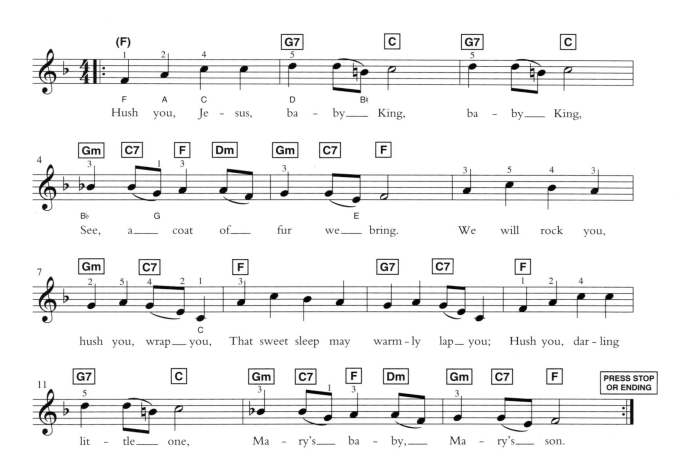

Reproduced by permission of Campion Press

UE 21 076L

| Style No. |
| Voice No. |

Silent Night

Music: Franz Gruber
Words: Anon.

| **Suggested Style:** Slow Waltz
 Suggested Voice: Pan Flute
 Tempo: c.88 beats per minute | Count THREE beats in a bar. The curved lines connecting some pairs of notes are called SLURS. Play smoothly from one note to the next. | We are in the key of C major; no black keys are needed. If singers find this too high, use **transpose** to lower the pitch. |

PLAY this introduction:

OR press INTRO. Start the keyboard introduction by playing a chord of C

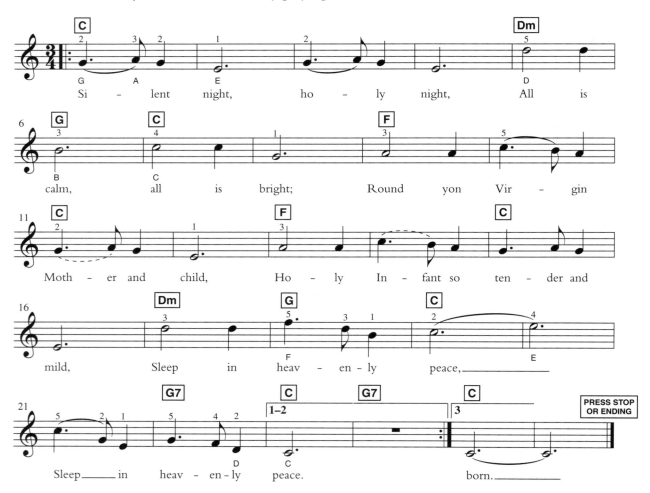

2. Silent night, holy night,
   Son of God, love's pure light;
   Radiant beams from Thy holy face,
   With the dawn of redeeming grace,
   Jesus, Lord, at Thy birth,
   Jesus, Lord, at Thy birth.

3. Silent night, holy night,
   Wond'rous star, lead Thy light;
   With the angels let us sing,
   Alleluia to our King;
   Christ the Saviour is born,
   Christ the Saviour is born.

UE 21 076L

The Virgin Mary had a Baby Boy

Words and Music: Trad. Trinidad

Suggested Style: Pop Reggae
Suggested Voice: Steel Drums
Tempo: c.130 beats per minute

Count a steady FOUR beats in a bar. This version includes the syncopations and variations of contemporary performances as well as a 2-bar "break" between verses.

We are in the key of G major. Look out for F♯s, the black key to the right of F.

PLAY this introduction:

OR press INTRO. Start the keyboard introduction by playing a chord of G

2. The angels sang when the baby born,
   The angels sang when the baby born,
   The angels sang when the baby born,
   And proclaim him the Saviour Jesus.
   He come from the glory, etc.

3. The wise men went where the baby born,
   The wise men went where the baby born,
   The wise men went where the baby born,
   And they say that his name was Jesus.
   He come from the glory, etc.

29

UE 21 076L

We Three Kings

Words and Music: John Henry Hopkins

Suggested Style: Jazz Waltz **Suggested Voice:** Shanai **Tempo:** c.132 beats per minute	Count THREE beats in a bar. Choose a faster tempo when you are familiar with the piece.	We are in the key of E minor in the verse and G major in the chorus. Both keys use F♯, the black key to the right of F.

PLAY this introduction:

OR press INTRO. Start the keyboard introduction by playing a chord of E minor

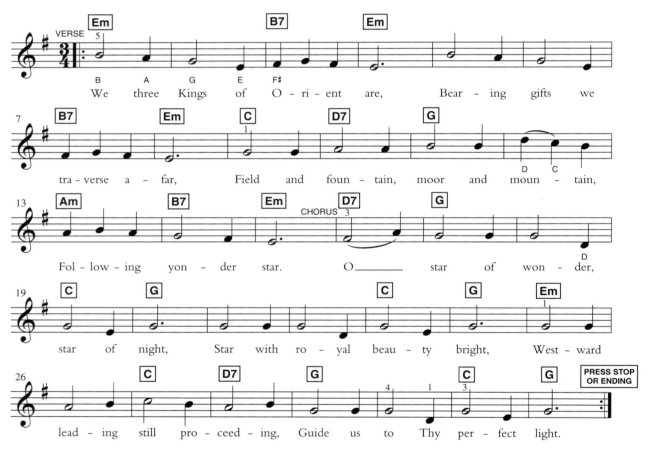

(GASPARD)

2. Born a king on Bethlehem plain,
   Gold I bring to crown him again,
   King for ever, ceasing never
   Over us all to reign.
   O star of wonder etc.

(BALTHAZAR)

4. Myrrh is mine; its bitter perfume
   Breathes a life of gathering gloom;
   Sorrowing, sighing, bleeding, dying,
   Sealed in a stone-cold tomb.
   O star of wonder etc.

(MELCHIOR)

3. Frankincense to offer have I,
   Incense owns a Deity nigh:
   Prayer and praising all men raising,
   Worship him, God on high.
   O star of wonder etc.

(ALL)

5. Glorious now behold him arise,
   King and God, and sacrifice.
   Heaven sing: 'Alleluia';
   'Alleluia' the earth replies.
   O star of wonder etc.

UE 21 076L

Style No.	
Voice No.	

We Wish you a Merry Christmas

Words and Music: Trad. English

Suggested Style: Musette
Suggested Voice: Crystal
Tempo: c.140 beats per minute

Count THREE beats in a bar. This carol needs to move along at a fairly good pace. Note that the verse and the refrain both begin on the "up-beat", the 3rd beat of the bar.

We are in the key of G major. Look out for F♯s, the black key to the right of F.

PLAY this introduction:

OR press INTRO. Start the keyboard introduction by playing a chord of G

2. Now bring us some figgy pudding,
   Now bring us some figgy pudding,
   Now bring us some figgy pudding,
   And bring it us here!
   Glad tidings, etc.

3. O we won't go until we've got some,
   No, we won't go until we've got some,
   We won't go until we've got some,
   So give it us here!
   Glad tidings, etc.

4. O we all like figgy pudding,
   Yes we all like figgy pudding,
   We all like figgy pudding,
   So bring it out here!
   Glad tidings, etc.

UE 21 076L

Style No.	
Voice No.	

While Shepherds Watched

Music: Trad. English
Words: Nahum Tate (1652–1715)

Suggested Style: 8-beat Pop **Suggested Voice:** Violin & harmony **Tempo:** c.86 beats per minute	Count FOUR beats in a bar. Note that the introduction and the verse begin on the 4th beat of the bar.

We are in the key of F major. Look out for B♭s, the black key to the left of B.

PLAY this introduction:

OR press INTRO. Start the keyboard introduction by playing a chord of F

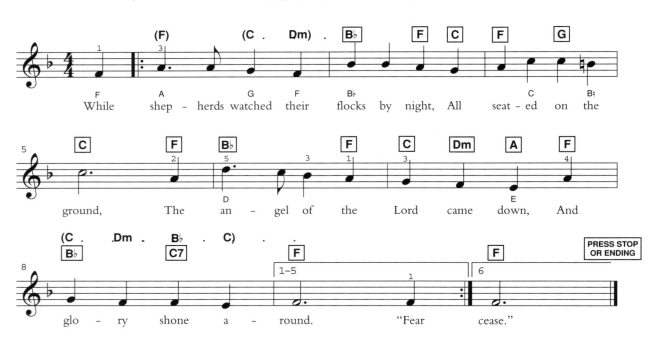

2. "Fear not," said he, for mighty dread
Had seized their troubled mind;
"Glad tidings of great joy I bring
To you and all mankind.

3. "To you in David's town this day
Is born of David's line,
The Saviour, who is Christ the Lord;
And this shall be the sign:

4. "The heavenly babe you there shall find
To human view displayed,
All meanly wrapped in swathing bands,
And in a manger laid."

5. Thus spake the seraph; and forthwith
Appeared a shining throng
Of angels praising God, who thus
Addressed their joyful song:

6. "All glory be to God on high,
And to the earth be peace;
Goodwill henceforth from heaven to men
Begin and never cease."

UE 21 076L

LVIII/01